READ, EXPLORE, AND DISCOVER

STEP UP

Fun learn-to-read stories and companion
activities to build confident readers!
PLUS flash cards and activities to practice the
words every young reader must know!

Senior Editor: Janet Sweet
Design/Production: Rebekah O. Lewis
Art Director: Moonhee Pak
Managing Editor: Stacey Faulkner

© 2010 Creative Teaching Press Inc., Huntington Beach, CA 92649
All rights reserved. Except as permitted under the United States Copyright, no part of this publication may be reproduced or distributed in any form or
by any means, or stored in a database or retrieval system, without prior written permission from the publisher, unless otherwise indicated.

Table of Contents

Learn to READ Tips

Helping Your Child Learn to READ

Reading is the most important skill your child needs for success in school and in life. Helping your child learn to **read, explore, and** discover the world of written language today ensures a bright and successful future for your child tomorrow.

You Have Already Taken the First Step

From infancy through the preschool years, your child has already learned valuable **pre-reading** skills at home just by interacting with you as you talk, sing, recite nursery rhymes, and read aloud from stories, street signs, restaurant menus—even food labels. Activities like these built the necessary groundwork for your child to learn the sounds and names for letters and words, and to connect information with printed words. Now your child is ready to take the next step to becoming a reader!

The READ Series Helps You with the Next Step

Your child's success as a beginning reader requires the right stories and reading materials at the right time. Faced with so many beginning-to-read choices in the marketplace, it is often difficult for parents to know which ones are best for their children. The **READ** series by Creative Teaching Press has been specifically designed with your child's and your needs in mind. Engaging stories and expertly developed companion materials support a confident transition into successful early reading. Once children make the exhilarating discovery that they can read by themselves, their reading skills soar and there is simply no stopping them!

About the READ Series

Young children are naturally drawn to images and ideas that are all about their world. The **READ Stories** in each workbook feature amusing characters and visually appealing illustrations that engage your child's attention and nurture reading development. Each story is designed to encourage and support your child's reading efforts by providing:

- High-interest topics to beginning readers
- Humorous or surprise endings that encourage rereading
- Predictable story lines with repeating text
- Exposure to repeating sound and word patterns in familiar tales and rhymes

The stories in each workbook feature bright-colored art and whimsical illustrations in a broad mix of styles that naturally appeal to young children. At the bottom of every story page are **READ Picture Clue Prompts**. These are short, simple questions that encourage your beginning reader to use picture clues that are embedded in the illustrations to derive meaning from the story. This is an important skill in enabling children to deepen their reading enjoyment, language development, and comprehension.

In addition, each workbook features **Companion READ Activities** designed to reinforce and extend the skills introduced in each story, including:

- Sight Words—to review the high-frequency words that your child must know by sight
- Phonics—to review letter sounds
- Vocabulary—to review new and unfamiliar words from each book
- Skill—to practice related learning skills from each book
- Activity—with easy directions to help your child create a collection of make-your-own mini-books related directly to the content and vocabulary of each story
- Encourage your child to read the books often to build reading fluency.

Each **READ** workbook also features **Activities, Word Lists, and Flash Cards** to help your child practice recognizing the **Words Every Reader Must Know**. These are the most commonly used words in the English language, making up nearly 75% of everything a young child reads. Typically these "must-know" words do not follow regular spelling rules or phonics patterns, which makes them very difficult for beginning readers to recognize or sound out. The **READ** activities are designed to help your child develop mastery, confidence, and fluency when encountering these words in both reading and writing.

Parent Suggestions to Help Your Child READ

Here are some parent-friendly ideas for helping to make your child's learning-to-read experience relaxed, enjoyable, and stimulating:

- First, it is important to remember that children do not have to know all their letters and sounds before you put a story in their hands. Children are learning a great deal about reading at this point.

- Next, introduce each story by looking at and discussing the pictures <u>before</u> reading the story. This is called a *picture walk,* and it helps your child get a sense of what the story will be about. A preview such as this will help your child become familiar with and hear the sound of certain vocabulary words before they appear in print, as well as make predictions about the story's ending.

- Then, read the story aloud to your child. Feel free to read it aloud more than once. Most importantly, read aloud with enthusiasm and expression, which helps your child become familiar with the sentence patterns, vocabulary words, and story line. This will build your child's confidence in his or her attempts to read the story independently.

- Now read the story with your child. Actively involve your child as you read together by:
  - » Pointing to the words as you read.
  - » Guiding your child's finger or having him or her point to the words as you read.
  - » Reading a page and inviting your child to point and repeat after you.
  - » Reading the story together.
  - » Reading the story and pausing often so your child can supply the next word.
  - » Praising and encouraging your child's effort.

- Finally, read alongside your child. This is the exciting step when your child reads the story alone! It usually occurs spontaneously while you are sharing the story, and it is an exhilarating moment for your child.

- Don't worry if your child doesn't read each word perfectly the first time. There will be plenty of chances to develop accuracy as your child reads the story again and again. Encourage your child to tackle difficult words or phrases by:
  - » Looking at the related illustrations for clues and taking a guess.
  - » Reading beyond the difficult word for helpful clues from the next sentence.
  - » Replacing the difficult word or phrase by saying aloud "blank" and asking your child what would sound right or make sense.
  - » Rereading the sentence.
  - » Looking at the first letter for a clue to the initial sound.
  - » Sounding out the word.

Who Will Help?

1 What is the mouse doing?

2 What is the mouse standing on?

R.E.A.D. Step Up • Gr. K–1 © 2010 Creative Teaching Press

"Who will help me pick the apples?"

1 Why does the mouse need help?

2 What is the blue and brown thing that holds the apples?

R.E.A.D. Step Up • Gr. K–1 © 2010 Creative Teaching Press

1. A white box points to each animal. Why are the animals' words in the boxes?

2. Why don't the animals help the mouse?

R.E.A.D. Step Up • Gr. K–1 © 2010 Creative Teaching Press

"Who will help me wash the apples?"

1 What tells you that this is a farm?

2 What is the thing that the mouse uses to get water?

R.E.A.D. Step Up • Gr. K–1 © 2010 Creative Teaching Press

1 Name 3 things that the cow is wearing.

2 How do you know it is a sunny day?

R.E.A.D. Step Up • Gr. K–1 © 2010 Creative Teaching Press

"Who will help me peel the apples?"

1 What does the word *peel* mean?

2 What tells you that the animals are on a porch?

R.E.A.D. Step Up • Gr. K–1 © 2010 Creative Teaching Press

1 What is the duck resting on?

2 Why won't the cow and the rabbit help the mouse?

R.E.A.D. Step Up • Gr. K–1 © 2010 Creative Teaching Press

"Who will help me cut the apples?"

1 Look at the small lines over the mouse's eyes. How does he probably feel?

2 What is he standing on?

R.E.A.D. Step Up • Gr. K–1 © 2010 Creative Teaching Press

"Not me!" said the cow.

1 Is the cow getting cold or warm food?

2 How do you know this?

R.E.A.D. Step Up • Gr. K–1 © 2010 Creative Teaching Press

"Not me!" said the duck.
"Not me!" said the rabbit.

1 Look at the pictures on pages 16 and 17.

2 Name 3 things that tell you the duck and the rabbit are outside.

R.E.A.D. Step Up • Gr. K–1 © 2010 Creative Teaching Press

1 Look at the mouse. What tells you that he is not happy with the other animals?

2 How do you know that he is almost done with the apples?

R.E.A.D. Step Up • Gr. K–1 © 2010 Creative Teaching Press

"Who will help me cook the apples?"

1 What tells you that the mouse needs help?

2 What does the white line over the black pot mean?

R.E.A.D. Step Up • Gr. K–1 © 2010 Creative Teaching Press

1 Do you think the other animals care about the apples?

2 Do you think they care about the mouse?

R.E.A.D. Step Up • Gr. K–1 © 2010 Creative Teaching Press

1 Do you think the mouse really wants help now?

2 Why do you think that?

R.E.A.D. Step Up • Gr. K–1 © 2010 Creative Teaching Press

1 How do you know that the duck, rabbit, and cow are ready to eat the applesauce?

2 What do you think will happen next?

R.E.A.D. Step Up • Gr. K–1 © 2010 Creative Teaching Press

1 Why does this ending seem right?

2 Do you think the duck, rabbit, and cow will help next time?

R.E.A.D. Step Up • Gr. K–1 © 2010 Creative Teaching Press

Who Will Help?

☼ Write **who, will** or **help** on each line.

"Who _____ help me pick flowers?" asked Cow.

"_____ will help me look for a bug?" asked Duck.

"Who will _____ me eat carrots?" asked Rabbit.

R.E.A.D. Step Up • Gr. K–1 © 2010 Creative Teaching Press

Words with ill

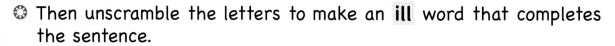

⚙ Trace **will** in the sentence.

⚙ Then unscramble the letters to make an **ill** word that completes the sentence.

Who _will_ help Mouse?

| i l |
| h l |

 We can walk up the ___ ___ ___ ___ .

| f l |
| i l |

I will ___ ___ ___ ___ ___ the glass.

| i g |
| l l |

 This is the fish's ___ ___ ___ ___ ___ .

| i j |
| l l |

 ___ ___ ___ ___ went up the hill

with Jack.

R.E.A.D. Step Up • Gr. K–1 © 2010 Creative Teaching Press

What Is Mouse Doing?

⚙ Write one **ing** action word to finish each sentence.

Word Box

| cutting | eating | cooking | picking | washing |

Mouse is _____ apples.

Mouse is _____ apples.

Mouse is _____ apples.

Mouse is _____ apples.

Mouse is _____ applesauce. Yum!

What Are They Saying?

☉ Look at the pictures. Trace **who** **will** **help**.

☉ Then write what each animal is saying inside the quotation marks **" "**.

" _Who will help_ ?"
asked Mouse.

" _____ _____ !" said Duck.

" _____ _____ !" said Rabbit.

" _____ _____ !" said Cow.

R.E.A.D. Step Up • Gr. K–1 © 2010 Creative Teaching Press

Make a Mini Book

- ✪ Cut along the <u>solid</u> lines.
- ✪ Fold on the <u>dotted</u> lines and staple.
- ✪ Write **help** in each blank.
- ✪ Write your name and draw yourself on page 8.

Who Will Help?
by
Danny

"Who will _____
me bake a cake?"
"Not me!" said the cow.

4

"Who will _____
me wrap the presents?"
"Not me!" said the duck.

5

"Who will help me
celebrate my birthday?"
"I will!" said _____ .

8

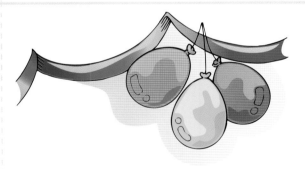

Who Will Help?

by

_____

1

R.E.A.D. Step Up • Gr. K–1 © 2010 Creative Teaching Press

Make a Mini Book

✂

"Who will _____ me blow up the balloons?"
"Not me!" said the sheep.

6

"Who will ___help___ me go to the store?"
"Not me!" said the pig.

3

Today is my birthday!

2

"Who will _____ me light the candles?"
"Not me!" said the cat.

7

28

She'll Be Coming Around the Mountain

1 What tells you that the woman and the cat will probably be driving?

2 What is the cat holding?

R.E.A.D. Step Up • Gr. K–1 © 2010 Creative Teaching Press

**She'll be coming around the mountain when she comes.
She'll be coming around the mountain when she comes.**

1 Do many people live around the mountain? How do you know?

2 Why would there be a road sign with a picture of a cow?

R.E.A.D. Step Up • Gr. K–1 © 2010 Creative Teaching Press

She'll be coming around the mountain.
She'll be coming around the mountain.
She'll be coming around the mountain
when she comes.

1 What tells you that the people on the mountain are farmers?

2 What is the red thing in front of the farmer?

R.E.A.D. Step Up • Gr. K–1 © 2010 Creative Teaching Press

She will drive a new red race car
when she comes.
She will drive a new red race car
when she comes.

1 What might tell you that the red car is going fast?

2 Why can't you see their faces?

R.E.A.D. Step Up • Gr. K–1 © 2010 Creative Teaching Press

She will drive a new red race car.
She will drive a new red race car.
She will drive a new red race car
when she comes.

1 How do you know that one of the cows is surprised?

2 Why would a cow need to wear a bell on the mountain?

R.E.A.D. Step Up • Gr. K–1 © 2010 Creative Teaching Press

She'll be wearing cool sunglasses
when she comes.
She'll be wearing cool sunglasses
when she comes.

She'll be wearing cool sunglasses.
She'll be wearing cool sunglasses.

She'll be wearing cool sunglasses
when she comes.

1 Look at the road. What kind of a ride would you have on that road?

2 Do you think it would be easy to drive fast there? Why?

R.E.A.D. Step Up • Gr. K–1 © 2010 Creative Teaching Press

1 Why would they wear sunglasses?

2 What tells you they are going down a hill now?

R.E.A.D. Step Up • Gr. K–1 © 2010 Creative Teaching Press

We will all go out to meet her
when she comes.
We will all go out to meet her
when she comes.

1 Why do you think the farmers and animals are running to meet her?

2 How can you tell that they are running?

R.E.A.D. Step Up • Gr. K–1 © 2010 Creative Teaching Press

We will all go out to meet her.
We will all go out to meet her.
We will all go out to meet her
when she comes.

1 Which animal on this page looks a little worried?

2 What might be a problem for that animal?

R.E.A.D. Step Up • Gr. K–1 © 2010 Creative Teaching Press

We will play some happy music when she comes.
We will play some happy music when she comes.

1 What is the thing that the farm girl is playing?

2 Find a silly animal detail that is funny on this page.

R.E.A.D. Step Up • Gr. K–1 © 2010 Creative Teaching Press

We will play some happy music.
We will play some happy music.
We will play some happy music
when she comes.

1 There are little lines around the woman's hands. What do they mean?

2 What is the word for a group that sings and plays music together?

R.E.A.D. Step Up • Gr. K–1 © 2010 Creative Teaching Press

We will all have cake and ice cream when she comes.

We will all have cake and ice cream when she comes.

1 What tells you that the cake is probably very sweet?

2 How do you know that the sheep likes cake and ice cream?

R.E.A.D. Step Up • Gr. K–1 © 2010 Creative Teaching Press

We will all have cake and ice cream.
We will all have cake and ice cream.
We will all have cake and ice cream
when she comes.

1 What is the horse doing with its cake?

2 How do you know that the cow is having fun?

R.E.A.D. Step Up • Gr. K–1 © 2010 Creative Teaching Press

We will have a great big party
when she comes.
We will have a great big party
when she comes.

1 Name 2 things on this page that tell you it is a party.

2 What is the thing that the cow is playing?

R.E.A.D. Step Up • Gr. K–1 © 2010 Creative Teaching Press

We will have a great big party.
We will have a great big party.
We will have a great big party
when she comes.

1 What are the dog and the farmer playing?

2 What is different about the farmer now?

R.E.A.D. Step Up • Gr. K–1 © 2010 Creative Teaching Press

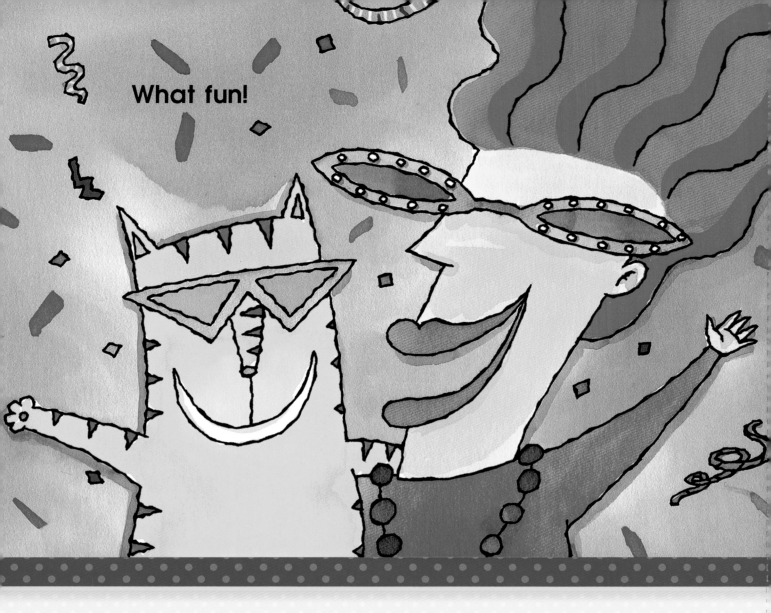

What fun!

1 What shape do you see all over the cat?

2 Do you think that the woman and the cat will stay on the mountain? Why or why not?

R.E.A.D. Step Up • Gr. K–1 © 2010 Creative Teaching Press

Sight Words

Here She Comes!

Write when , she , or comes to finish each sentence.

She will drive a new red race

car [   ] she comes.

She'll be wearing cool sunglasses

when [   ] comes.

We will all go out to meet her

when she [   ] .

We will play some happy music

[   ] [   ] [   ] .

R.E.A.D. Step Up • Gr. K–1 © 2010 Creative Teaching Press

She'll Be Coming Around the Mountain

Around the Mountain

✹ Write ou to finish the words.

✹ Circle the six ou words in the puzzle below.

f[ ]nd

ar[ ]nd

ab[ ]t

s[ ]nd

m[ ]ntain

gr[ ]nd

b	s	r	t	o	p	n	d	x	a
m	o	u	n	t	a	i	n	g	b
n	u	p	u	w	r	p	i	m	o
t	n	k	g	r	o	u	n	d	u
s	d	u	r	y	u	v	a	o	t
c	e	f	o	u	n	d	q	s	l
o	s	w	i	n	d	g	i	r	p

R.E.A.D. Step Up • Gr. K–1 © 2010 Creative Teaching Press

She'll Be Coming Around the Mountain

Who Is She?

☼ Write about this funny lady.

☼ Finish each sentence.

☼ Read your story to a friend.

Here is a very funny lady!

Her name is _____.

She has _____

_____.

She likes to _____

_____.

She came around the mountain to _____

_____.

R.E.A.D. Step Up • Gr. K–1 © 2010 Creative Teaching Press

Let's Practice Contractions

○ Draw a line from the words to the matching contractions.

○ Then write one of the contractions in each sentence.

she will ○   ○ we'll

we will ○   ○ they'll

he will ○   ○ she'll

they will ○   ○ he'll

_____ all have cake and ice cream.

_____ be coming around the mountain.

_____ play music.

_____ all have a party!

R.E.A.D. Step Up • Gr. K–1 © 2010 Creative Teaching Press

Make a Mini Book

- Cut along the <u>solid</u> lines.
- Fold on the <u>dotted</u> lines and staple.
- Finish the **ing** words on page 2.

We are going to meet her.

4

We are playing music.

5

What fun!

8

What Are We Doing?

1

49

Make a Mini Book

She'll Be Coming Around the Mountain

We are having cake and ice cream.

6

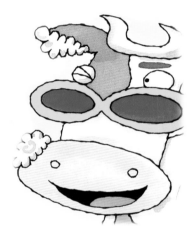

We are wearing sunglasses.

3

Write **-ing** to finish each word.

wear ___ ___ ___

go ___ ___ ___

play ___ ___ ___

hav ___ ___ ___

danc ___ ___ ___

2

We are dancing.

7

R.E.A.D. Step Up • Gr. K–1 © 2010 Creative Teaching Press

Lunch with Cat and Dog

1 What is Cat holding?

2 Why is Cat holding it over the apples?

R.E.A.D. Step Up • Gr. K–1 © 2010 Creative Teaching Press

"A pizza!
I want the most!" said Cat.

1 What tells you that Cat likes pizza?

2 What does the word *most* mean?

R.E.A.D. Step Up • Gr. K–1 © 2010 Creative Teaching Press

"OK," said Dog.
"Two pieces for you
and one piece for me."

1 Look at the pizza. Will Cat get the most?

2 How are the pieces different and yet still
the same?

R.E.A.D. Step Up • Gr. K–1 © 2010 Creative Teaching Press

"Yes!" said Cat.

1. There are words in white bubbles over Cat's head. What does that mean?

2. Why is Cat so happy?

R.E.A.D. Step Up • Gr. K–1 © 2010 Creative Teaching Press

"Watermelon!
I want the most!" yelled Cat.

1 How do you know that Cat likes watermelon?

2 What do the little black lines by Cat's hands mean?

R.E.A.D. Step Up • Gr. K–1 © 2010 Creative Teaching Press

"OK," said Dog.
"Three pieces for you
and one piece for me."

1 What does Dog do here that tells you he is smart?

2 Do you think Dog is fair or sneaky? Why?

R.E.A.D. Step Up • Gr. K–1 © 2010 Creative Teaching Press

"Goody!" said Cat.

1 How do you know that Dog is smarter than Cat?

2 What are the little black things on the table?

R.E.A.D. Step Up • Gr. K–1 © 2010 Creative Teaching Press

"Chocolate milk!
I want the most!" begged Cat.

1 What tells you that Cat is begging?

2 Why do you think Cat does this?

R.E.A.D. Step Up • Gr. K–1 © 2010 Creative Teaching Press

"OK," said Dog.
"A big glass for you
and a little glass for me."

1 What does Dog mean when he says "a big glass for you"?

2 Why will Cat think she is getting more than Dog?

R.E.A.D. Step Up • Gr. K–1 © 2010 Creative Teaching Press

"Cool!" said Cat.

1 What does "Glug! Glug!" over Cat's head mean?

2 How is the way Dog drinks different from the way Cat drinks?

R.E.A.D. Step Up • Gr. K–1 © 2010 Creative Teaching Press

"A big cookie!
I want the most!" screamed Cat.

1 Look at Dog. What tells you that
Cat screamed?

2 How do you think Dog will cut the cookie?

R.E.A.D. Step Up • Gr. K–1 © 2010 Creative Teaching Press

"OK," said Dog.
"Four pieces for you
and two pieces for me."

1 Look at Dog. What tells you that he is working hard on this?

2 What do you think the brown spots are on the cookie?

R.E.A.D. Step Up • Gr. K–1 © 2010 Creative Teaching Press

"Hooray!" said Cat.

1 How are Dog's 2 pieces the same as Cat's 4 pieces?

2 What are the little brown things on the table?

R.E.A.D. Step Up • Gr. K–1 © 2010 Creative Teaching Press

"A cake!
I want the most!" demanded Cat.

1 Do you think it is easy to make Cat happy?

2 What tells you that Dog probably made the cake?

R.E.A.D. Step Up • Gr. K–1 © 2010 Creative Teaching Press

"OK," said Dog.
"Eight pieces for you
and two pieces for me."

1 Why does Dog look happy?

2 How many pieces did Dog cut in all?

R.E.A.D. Step Up • Gr. K–1 © 2010 Creative Teaching Press

"I'm full!" said Cat.
"Me too!" said Dog.

1 How can you tell that Cat and Dog are full?

2 Dog is winking his eye. Why? What does that mean?

R.E.A.D. Step Up • Gr. K–1 © 2010 Creative Teaching Press

A Good Lunch

◯ Write **piece** on each line to finish the poem.

◯ Then draw lines to match the words with the pictures below.

One _____ of fruit,

One _____ of meat,

One _____ of cake,

Makes a good lunch to eat!

   •   •   a piece of pizza

   •   •   a piece of bread

   •   •   a piece of pie

   •   •   a piece of candy

R.E.A.D. Step Up • Gr. K–1 © 2010 Creative Teaching Press

long a Words

⚙ Circle the **long a** words in each sentence.

Dog gave Cat
8 pieces of cake.

Dog made
a pizza. He
gave two
pieces to Cat.

Yes!
Two pieces!

Hooray!

"Hooray!" said Cat.
"Dog came here and
baked a big cookie."

R.E.A.D. Step Up • Gr. K–1 © 2010 Creative Teaching Press

How Did Cat Say It?

⚙ Write a word from the Word Box to complete each sentence.

Word Box

yelled	said	begged

"I like pizza,"

_____ Cat.

"I want watermelon!"

_____ Cat.

"Please give me some chocolate milk,"

_____ Cat.

R.E.A.D. Step Up • Gr. K–1 © 2010 Creative Teaching Press

Words That Sound the Same

○ Some words sound the same, but they are spelled differently, and mean different things.

see   **sea**

○ Write the correct word in each sentence.

meet	meat

I will _____ you at school.

I had _____ for dinner.

be	bee

A _____ is on the flower.

Will you _____ home at six?

here	hear

_____ is a cat.

Please come _____ me sing.

R.E.A.D. Step Up • Gr. K–1 © 2010 Creative Teaching Press

Make a Mini Book

- Cut along the <u>solid</u> lines.
- Fold on the <u>dotted</u> lines and staple.
- Write or draw what you like to eat for lunch on page 8.
- Read your book!

Lunch with
Cat and Dog

by

_____Dee_____

Cat and Dog

had a cookie for lunch.

4

5

**Lunch with
Cat and Dog**

by

_____

8

1

R.E.A.D. Step Up • Gr. K–1 © 2010 Creative Teaching Press

Make a Mini Book

Cat and Dog had chocolate milk for lunch.

6

Cat and Dog had watermelon for lunch.

3

Cat and Dog had pizza for lunch.

2

What do you eat for lunch?

7

R.E.A.D. Step Up • Gr. K–1 © 2010 Creative Teaching Press

Five Little Monsters

1 What tells you that these are monsters?

2 Do you think the five little monsters will be good or bad? Why?

R.E.A.D. Step Up • Gr. K–1 © 2010 Creative Teaching Press

Five little monsters swinging from the tree,

1 How many monsters are hanging upside down?

2 Do you think this is a safe way to play in a tree?

R.E.A.D. Step Up • Gr. K–1 © 2010 Creative Teaching Press

one fell off and bumped her knee.

1 What do the little lines by her tail and hand mean?

2 Look at her face. How does she feel?

R.E.A.D. Step Up • Gr. K–1 © 2010 Creative Teaching Press

**Daddy called the doctor
and the doctor agreed,**

1 What tells you that Daddy is worried?

2 What is the thing that hangs from his neck?

R.E.A.D. Step Up • Gr. K–1 © 2010 Creative Teaching Press

"No more monsters swinging from the tree!"

1 What tells you that the doctor means what he says?

2 The thing that hangs from his neck is a stethoscope. Why does a doctor use that?

R.E.A.D. Step Up • Gr. K–1 © 2010 Creative Teaching Press

**Four little monsters
swinging from the tree,**

1 What part of the tree are they holding onto?

2 How do you know that they are having fun?

R.E.A.D. Step Up • Gr. K–1 © 2010 Creative Teaching Press

one fell off and bumped his knee.

1 What do the little stars and lines over his knee mean?

2 How does he show that he is hurt?

R.E.A.D. Step Up • Gr. K–1 © 2010 Creative Teaching Press

**Mommy called the doctor
and the doctor agreed,**

1 How do you know that Mommy is worried?

2 What is the white thing that Mommy is wearing?

R.E.A.D. Step Up • Gr. K–1 © 2010 Creative Teaching Press

"No more monsters swinging from the tree!"

1 Name 2 things that tell you he is a doctor.

2 Why do you think he has so many books?

R.E.A.D. Step Up • Gr. K–1 © 2010 Creative Teaching Press

Three little monsters
swinging from the tree,
one fell off and
bumped her knee.

1 How many little monsters have fallen by now?

2 Are the last 2 little monsters worried about falling?

R.E.A.D. Step Up • Gr. K–1 © 2010 Creative Teaching Press

Grandma called the doctor and the doctor agreed, "No more monsters swinging from the tree!"

1 Does it help when the big monsters call the doctor?

2 Why do you think a different big monster calls each time?

R.E.A.D. Step Up • Gr. K–1 © 2010 Creative Teaching Press

Two little monsters swinging from the tree,

one fell off and bumped his knee.

1 Why does the yellow monster have his eyes closed?

2 What do you think will probably happen to the pink monster?

R.E.A.D. Step Up • Gr. K–1 © 2010 Creative Teaching Press

Grandpa called the doctor and the doctor agreed, "No more monsters swinging from the tree!"

1 How do you know that Grandpa is old?

2 What is the doctor probably thinking?

R.E.A.D. Step Up • Gr. K–1 © 2010 Creative Teaching Press

One little monster swinging from the tree, she fell off and bumped her knee.

1 She did not mean to fall. How do you know that?

2 When would you say "Oops"?

R.E.A.D. Step Up • Gr. K–1 © 2010 Creative Teaching Press

The family called the doctor and the doctor agreed . . .

1 What do you think will happen next?

2 There are big and little monsters in the family. How many are there in all?

R.E.A.D. Step Up • Gr. K–1 © 2010 Creative Teaching Press

1 What does the picture on the tree mean?

2 Look closely at the little monsters. What are 2 of them thinking about doing?

R.E.A.D. Step Up • Gr. K–1 © 2010 Creative Teaching Press

What Word Is Missing?

☼ Write a word from the Word Box to finish the sentences.

Word Box

called	one	from	little

Four _____ monsters swinging from the tree,

_____ fell off and bumped his knee.

Mommy _____ the doctor and the doctor agreed,

"No more monsters swinging _____ the tree!"

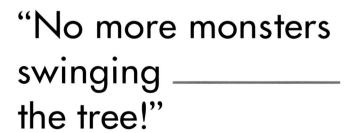

R.E.A.D. Step Up • Gr. K–1 © 2010 Creative Teaching Press

kn Words

Five Little Monsters

✪ Write **kn** on the lines to make words that begin with the /**n**/ sound.

✪ Then write a **kn** word to finish each sentence.

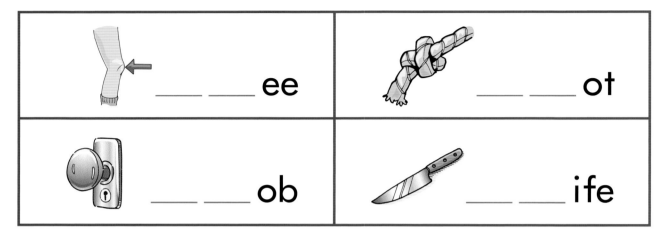

_____ _____ ee	_____ _____ ot
_____ _____ ob	_____ _____ ife

He bumped his _____.

I can make a _____.

Mom cut an apple
with a _____.

Turn the _____ to open the door.

R.E.A.D. Step Up • Gr. K–1 © 2010 Creative Teaching Press

All in the Family

Five Little Monsters

- ✿ Label the members of the monster family with the words from the Word Box.

- ✿ Write a sentence about a family member on the lines below.

Word Box

Grandfather	Mother	Father	Grandmother

Daddy

_____

_____

Grandpa

Grandma

_____

_____

Mommy

_____

_____

R.E.A.D. Step Up • Gr. K–1 © 2010 Creative Teaching Press

Boy and Girl Monsters

○ Write **he**, **she**, **his**, or **her** in each box.

This is a little girl monster.

☐ is purple.

☐ fell and

bumped ☐ knee.

This is a little boy monster.

☐ is blue.

But ☐ nose is green

and ☐ hair is black.

☐ is swinging

from the tree.

Make a Mini Book

☼ Cut along the <u>solid</u> lines.

☼ Fold on the <u>dotted</u> lines and staple.

☼ Add words and/or drawings to finish the book.

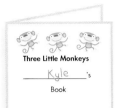

_____ called the doctor and the doctor said, "No more monkeys jumping on the bed!"

4

_____ little _____ jumping on the bed.

5

"No more _____ jumping on the bed!"

8

Three Little Monkeys

_____'s

Book

1

R.E.A.D. Step Up • Gr. K–1 © 2010 Creative Teaching Press

Make a Mini Book

✂

_____ fell off and
bumped his head.

6

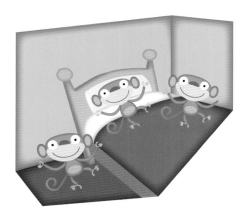

One fell off and
bumped his head.

3

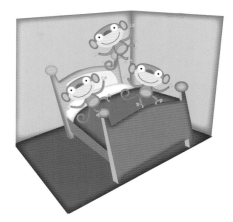

_____ little monkeys,
jumping on the bed.

2

_____ called the
doctor, and the doctor said,

7

R.E.A.D. Step Up • Gr. K–1 © 2010 Creative Teaching Press

First 100 Words Every Reader Must Know

a	did	if	on	this
about	do	in	one	three
after	down	is	or	to
again	eat	it	other	two
all	for	just	our	up
an	from	know	out	us
and	get	like	put	very
any	give	little	said	was
are	go	long	see	we
as	good	make	she	were
at	had	man	so	what
be	has	many	some	when
been	have	me	take	which
before	he	much	that	who
boy	her	my	the	will
but	here	new	their	with
by	him	no	them	work
can	his	not	then	would
come	how	of	there	you
day	I	old	they	your

R.E.A.D. Step Up • Gr. K–1 © 2010 Creative Teaching Press

Second 100 Words Every Reader Must Know

also	each	left	own	sure
am	ear	let	people	tell
another	end	live	play	than
away	far	look	please	these
back	find	made	present	thing
ball	first	may	pretty	think
because	five	men	ran	too
best	found	more	read	tree
better	four	morning	red	under
big	friend	most	right	until
black	girl	mother	run	upon
book	got	must	saw	use
both	hand	name	say	want
box	high	near	school	way
bring	home	never	seem	where
call	house	next	shall	while
came	into	night	should	white
color	kind	only	soon	why
could	last	open	stand	wish
dear	leave	over	such	year

R.E.A.D. Step Up • Gr. K–1 © 2010 Creative Teaching Press

Third 100 Words Every Reader Must Know

along	don't	grow	off	stop
always	door	happy	once	ten
anything	dress	hard	order	thank
around	early	hat	pair	third
ask	eight	head	part	those
ate	every	hear	ride	though
bed	eyes	help	round	today
brown	face	hold	same	took
buy	fall	hope	sat	town
car	fast	hot	second	try
carry	fat	jump	set	turn
clean	fine	keep	seven	walk
close	fire	letter	show	warm
clothes	fly	longer	sing	wash
coat	food	love	sister	water
cold	full	might	sit	woman
cut	funny	money	six	write
didn't	gave	myself	sleep	yellow
does	goes	now	small	yes
dog	green	o'clock	start	yesterday

97

Words Every Reader Must Know
in each READ Story

Who Will Help?

who	me	cut	no	by
will	the	said	I	myself
help	not	eat	all	

She'll Be Coming Around the Mountain

be	come(s)	car	to	have
around	will	we	her	big
the	a	all	play	what
when	new	go	some	
she	red	out	happy	

Lunch with Cat and Dog

with	want	for	three	eight
and	the	you	big	full
dog	most	one	little	too
a	said	me	four	
I	two	yes	love	

Five Little Monsters

five	tree	her	his	those
little	one	no	three	away
from	off	more	two	that
the	and	four	keep	

R.E.A.D. Step Up • Gr. K–1 © 2010 Creative Teaching Press

Sentence Skills

Words Every Reader Must Know

✪ Write the missing word in each sentence.

✪ Use the words from the word box.

Word Box

| most | think | thing | went | come |

1 I _____ that is good.

2 Tom and I _____ for a walk.

3 What is that _____?

4 Please _____ over here.

5 Cat wants the _____ food.

R.E.A.D. Step Up • Gr. K–1 © 2010 Creative Teaching Press

Sentence Skills

Words Every Reader Must Know

☼ Write the missing word in each sentence.

☼ Use the words from the word box.

Word Box

than	that	pretty	there	Where

1 _____ is he?

2 Two boys live over _____.

3 Which book is _____?

4 Her dog is bigger _____ my dog.

5 She has a _____ name.

R.E.A.D. Step Up • Gr. K–1 © 2010 Creative Teaching Press

Sentence Skills

Words Every Reader Must Know

☼ Write the missing word in each sentence.

☼ Use the words from the word box.

Word Box

too	find	to	five	another

1 We want _____ dog.

2 There are _____ cats.

3 That is _____ hot to eat.

4 Pat came _____ my house.

5 Did you _____ the toy?

R.E.A.D. Step Up • Gr. K–1 © 2010 Creative Teaching Press

Sentence Skills

Words Every Reader Must Know

✦ These sentences need your help. Put the words back in order so each sentence makes sense. The first one is done for you.

Hint: The first word of the sentence will start with a capital letter. The last word of the sentence will end in a "." or a "?".

1 They   are   here.   not

They are not here.

2 Here   my   is   school.

_____

3 you   Do   dogs?   like

_____

4 She   soon.   leave   can

_____

R.E.A.D. Step Up • Gr. K-1 © 2010 Creative Teaching Press

Sentence Skills

Words Every Reader Must Know

⚙ These sentences need your help. Put the words back in order so each sentence makes sense.

Hint: The first word of the sentence will start with a capital letter. The last word of the sentence will end in a "." or a "?".

1 it.   I   about   know

_____

2 you?   old   How   are

_____

3 box.   take   Please   this

_____

4 here.   right   It   goes

_____

R.E.A.D. Step Up • Gr. K–1 © 2010 Creative Teaching Press

Sentence Skills

Words Every Reader Must Know

These sentences need your help. Put the words back in order so each sentence makes sense.

Hint: The first word of the sentence will start with a capital letter. The last word of the sentence will end in a "." or a "?".

1 My   me   mother   home.   took

_____

2 put   that   Did   away?   you

_____

3 door.   Please   the   close

_____

4 Should   now?   we   go   home

_____

R.E.A.D. Step Up • Gr. K–1 © 2010 Creative Teaching Press

Sentence Skills

Words Every Reader Must Know

✿ These sentences need your help. Put the words back in order so each sentence makes sense.

Hint: The first word of the sentence will start with a capital letter. The last word of the sentence will end in a "." or a "?".

1 will   at   We   night.   leave

_____

2 run   to   He   fast.   likes

_____

3 buy   she   Can   book?   a

_____

4 Come   me   with   school.   to

_____

R.E.A.D. Step Up • Gr. K–1 © 2010 Creative Teaching Press

Flash Card Game Ideas

Words Every Reader Must Know

Flash cards for the Second 100 Words Every Reader Must Know appear on the following pages to support beginning readers in First Grade and Second Grade. Here are some game ideas for using the flash cards.

Play a sorting game

- Sort the flash cards into alphabetical order.
- Sort the flash cards by words that begin with the same letter.
- Sort the flash cards by words that rhyme. Think of additional words that rhyme and say them aloud or write them down.

Play a memory game

- Before cutting apart the flash cards, make a photocopy of each page to create a set of one-sided cards. Create a set of game cards by pulling out just one pair of cards for each beginning letter found in the flash cards. Turn these cards facedown to play a memory game. Each player takes a turn by turning over two cards at a time to read aloud the pair of words. If both words begin with the same letter, then that player gets to keep the pair of cards and take another turn. If the words do not begin with the same letter, then the next player gets to take a turn. The game continues until all the pairs of cards have been correctly paired.
- As a variation of this game, players must read aloud the pair of words and use each word in a sentence.

Other activities

- Use a timer to see how quickly each word can be read aloud. Begin with a small number of cards at first. Then add more cards as speed and confidence increases.
- Brainstorm another word that begins with the same sound as each flash card word.
- Use the blank flash cards to add other words to the flash card set.

R.E.A.D. Step Up • Gr. K–1 © 2010 Creative Teaching Press

also	am
another	away
back	ball
because	best
better	big

R.E.A.D. Step Up • Gr. K–1 © 2010 Creative Teaching Press

black	book
both	box
bring	call
came	color
could	dear

R.E.A.D. Step Up • Gr. K–1 © 2010 Creative Teaching Press

each	ear
end	far
find	first
five	found
four	friend

R.E.A.D. Step Up • Gr. K–1 © 2010 Creative Teaching Press

girl	got
hand	high
home	house
into	kind
last	leave

left	let
live	look
made	may
men	more
morning	most

R.E.A.D. Step Up • Gr. K–1 © 2010 Creative Teaching Press

mother	must
name	near
never	next
night	only
open	over

R.E.A.D. Step Up • Gr. K–1 © 2010 Creative Teaching Press

own	people
play	please
present	pretty
ran	read
red	right

R.E.A.D. Step Up • Gr. K–1 © 2010 Creative Teaching Press

run	saw
say	school
seem	shall
should	soon
stand	such

R.E.A.D. Step Up • Gr. K–1 © 2010 Creative Teaching Press

sure	tell
than	these
thing	think
too	tree
under	until

R.E.A.D. Step Up • Gr. K–1 © 2010 Creative Teaching Press

upon	use
want	way
where	while
white	why
wish	year

R.E.A.D. Step Up • Gr. K–1 © 2010 Creative Teaching Press

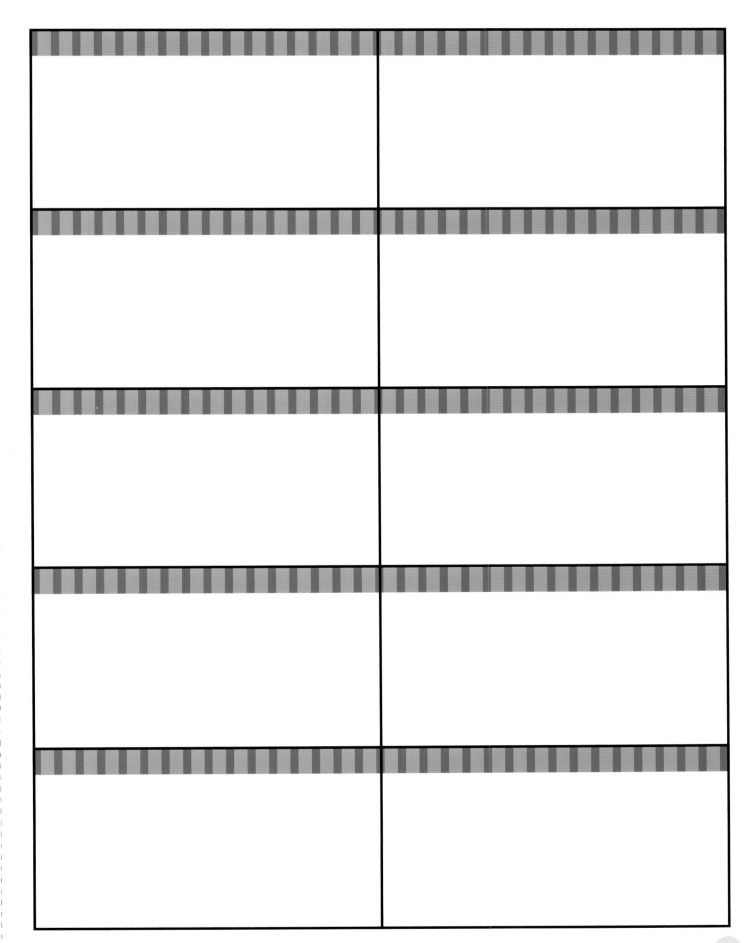

R.E.A.D. Step Up • Gr. K–1 © 2010 Creative Teaching Press

Answer Key READ Story Questions

Who Will Help?

PAGE 7

- Picking apples
- A ladder

PAGE 8

- There are a lot of apples; he is small.
- A basket

PAGE 9

- To tell you that each animal is talking; to tell what each animal says
- Possible answers: They want to play instead of work; they are lazy.

PAGE 10

- Barn; water pump; farm animals
- A pump

PAGE 11

- Fins; swim mask; swimsuit; water ring
- The rabbit is wearing sunglasses.

PAGE 12

- To take the skin off
- Porch railing; trees outside; porch steps

PAGE 13

- A hammock
- They are playing a game of checkers.

PAGE 14

- Possible answers: Angry, frustrated
- A stool

PAGE 15

- Cold food
- Possible answers: Cheese and juice are cold.

PAGE 16

- Porch; trees; front door is open

PAGE 17

- Not smiling; hands on his hips; looks mad
- The apple basket is empty.

PAGE 18

- Possible answers: He has trouble reaching the stove; he is on a ladder.
- The pot is hot; the apples are hot.

PAGE 19

- Possible answers: No—too much work; yes—if they can eat them
- No

PAGE 20

- Possible answers: Probably not; maybe
- Reasons should support the above answer.

PAGE 21

- They have spoons.
- Possible answers: The mouse will or won't share.

PAGE 22

- The animals didn't help the mouse, so they shouldn't get any applesauce.
- Possible answers: Yes—they learned their lesson; no—they don't like to work.

She'll Be Coming Around the Mountain

PAGE 29

- Possible answers: They are wearing sunglasses; they have a map.
- A map

Answer Key READ Story Questions

PAGE 30

- No, there aren't many houses.
- To warn drivers to look out for cows near the road

PAGE 31

- They are dressed like farmers; there is a cow and sheep in the picture.
- A wheelbarrow

PAGE 32

- The woman's hair is flying up.
- Their faces are behind the windshield.

PAGE 33

- Its eyes are wide open.
- So the farmer will know where the cow is; so the cow won't get lost

PAGE 34

- A hilly, bumpy ride
- Possible answers: No—because it is too hilly; yes—because it is a race car.

PAGE 35

- Possible answers: To be cool; to protect their eyes
- The road behind them is higher.

PAGE 36

- Possible answers: They know who she is; they are happy to see her.
- Their arms and legs are way out in front; the sheep's ears are pushed back.

PAGE 37

- The red bird with its eyes open
- Cats like to hunt birds.

PAGE 38

- A violin; a fiddle
- The chicken wearing sunglasses; the cow singing

PAGE 39

- She is clapping.
- A band

PAGE 40

- Possible answers: Cherries; lots of icing
- It is licking its lips.

PAGE 41

- Throwing it at the cow
- Possible answers: It is wearing sunglasses; it is laughing.

PAGE 42

- Party hat; music; dancing; having fun
- A drum (bongos)

PAGE 43

- Guitars
- He is wearing sunglasses; he is playing the guitar.

PAGE 44

- A triangle
- Possible answers: Stay—because they are having fun; leave—because they have to go home

Lunch with Cat and Dog

PAGE 51

- A ruler
- To measure how big they are

PAGE 52

- Smiling; clapping; the little heart
- The biggest amount of something

Answer Key READ Story Questions

PAGE 53

- No
- Dog cut 2 smaller pieces for Cat that equal the 1 bigger piece for himself.

PAGE 54

- That is what she is thinking; she is not saying the words aloud.
- Possible answers: She thinks she got the most pizza.

PAGE 55

- Her mouth is wide open; she's smiling.
- She is moving her hands.

PAGE 56

- He made Cat's 3 pieces the same size as his 1 piece.
- Possible answers: Fair—both of them get the same amount; sneaky—he is tricking Cat into thinking she gets the most.

PAGE 57

- Cat does not realize that she gets the same amount as Dog.
- Watermelon seeds

PAGE 58

- She is on her knees holding her hands.
- Possible answers: She likes chocolate milk; she wants the most.

PAGE 59

- That her glass is taller than his glass
- Because her glass looks bigger than his

PAGE 60

- That cat is a noisy drinker
- Dog uses a napkin to be tidy.

PAGE 61

- His ears and tail are pushed back.
- Possible answers: Just like he shared before

PAGE 62

- His tongue is out; he looks like he is really concentrating.
- Chocolate chips

PAGE 63

- His 2 pieces equal the same amount as Cat's 4 pieces.
- Cookie crumbs

PAGE 64

- Possible answers: No—Dog has to work hard to please Cat; Yes—Dog makes it look easy.
- He is wearing a baker's hat.

PAGE 65

- He divided the cake equally.
- 10

PAGE 66

- Hands on their stomachs
- Possible answer: That he was able to get as much food as Cat

Five Little Monsters

PAGE 73

- Possible answers: Tails, funny noses, fangs
- Possible answers: Good because they look happy; bad because they're little monsters

PAGE 74

- 2—the purple one and the blue one
- No

Answer Key READ Story Questions

PAGE 75

- That she is falling
- Worried; afraid; surprised

PAGE 76

- His eyes; his finger in his mouth
- A necktie

PAGE 77

- His arm is in the air; he is pointing his finger.
- To listen to your heart

PAGE 78

- A branch
- They are laughing and playing around.

PAGE 79

- His knee is hurt.
- He is crying; he says, "Ow!"

PAGE 80

- Possible answers: Her eyes; her hand on her face
- An apron

PAGE 81

- Stethoscope; doctor clothes; MD degree on the wall
- Possible answers: To find answers; to get help

PAGE 82

- 3
- No

PAGE 83

- Possible answers: No—nothing changes; yes—they get advice.
- Possible answers: They are taking turns; no one wants to call again and again.

PAGE 84

- He is afraid; he does not want to look.
- She will probably be the next one to fall.

PAGE 85

- He is bald and uses a cane.
- Possible answers: That another little monster fell again; that he wishes the family would listen to his advice

PAGE 86

- She says "Oops!"
- Possible answers: When making a mistake

PAGE 87

- The doctor will say, "No more monsters swinging from the tree!"
- 9

PAGE 88

- No monsters allowed
- Swinging on another tree

Answer Key **READ** Companion Activities

Who Will Help?

☼ Write **who**, **will** or **help** on each line.

"Who __will__ help
me pick flowers?"
asked Cow.

" __Who__ will help
me look for a bug?"
asked Duck.

"Who will __help__
me eat carrots?"
asked Rabbit.

23

Words with ill

☼ Trace **will** in the sentence.

☼ Then unscramble the letters to make an **ill** word that completes the sentence.

Who __will__ help Mouse?

| i l |
| h l | We can walk up the h i l l .

| f l |
| i l | I will f i l l the glass.

| i g |
| l l | This is the fish's g i l l .

| i j |
| l l | J i l l went up the hill
with Jack.

24

What Is Mouse Doing?

☼ Write one **ing** action word to finish each sentence.

Word Box

| cutting | eating | cooking | picking | washing |

Mouse is __picking__ apples.

Mouse is __washing__ apples.

Mouse is __cutting__ apples.

Mouse is __cooking__ apples.

Mouse is __eating__
applesauce. Yum!

25

What Are They Saying?

☼ Look at the pictures. Trace **who will help**.

☼ Then write what each animal is saying inside the quotation marks " ".

" __Who__ __will__ __help__ ?"
asked Mouse.

" __Not__ __me__ !" said Duck.

" __Not__ __me__ !" said Rabbit.

" __Not__ __me__ !" said Cow.

26

Answer Key **READ** Companion Activities

Sight Words

Here She Comes!

☼ Write when, she, or comes to finish each sentence.

She will drive a new red race car **when** she comes.

She'll be wearing cool sunglasses when **she** comes.

We will all go out to meet her when she **comes**.

We will play some happy music **when she comes**.

45

Phonics

Around the Mountain

☼ Write **ou** to finish the words.
☼ Circle the six **ou** words in the puzzle below.

f**ou**nd   ab**ou**t

ar**ou**nd

s**ou**nd   m**ou**ntain

gr**ou**nd

b	s	r	t	o	p	n	d	x	a
m	o	u	n	t	a	i	n	g	b
n	u	p	u	w	r	p	i	m	o
t	n	k	g	r	o	u	n	d	u
s	d	u	r	y	u	v	a	o	t
c	e	f	o	u	n	d	q	s	l
o	s	w	i	n	d	g	i	r	p

46

Vocabulary

Who Is She?

☼ Write about this funny lady.
☼ Finish each sentence.
☼ Read your story to a friend.

Here is a very funny lady!

Her name is _Answers will vary._

She has _Answers will vary._

_____

She likes to _Answers will vary._

_____

She came around the mountain to _____

Answers will vary.

47

Skill

Let's Practice Contractions

☼ Draw a line from the words to the matching contractions.
☼ Then write one of the contractions in each sentence.

she will   we'll
we will   they'll
he will   she'll
they will   he'll

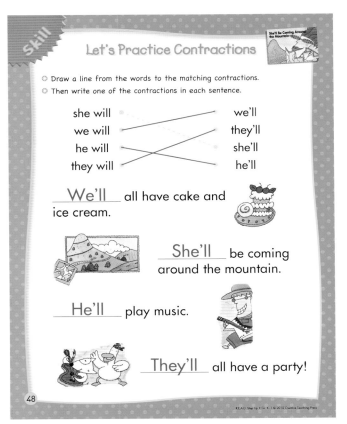

_We'll_ all have cake and ice cream.

She'll be coming around the mountain.

_He'll_ play music.

They'll all have a party!

48

Answer Key READ Companion Activities

Sight Words

A Good Lunch

- Write **piece** on each line to finish the poem.
- Then draw lines to match the words with the pictures below.

One <u>piece</u> of fruit,

One <u>piece</u> of meat,

One <u>piece</u> of cake,

Makes a good lunch to eat!

a piece of pizza

a piece of bread

a piece of pie

a piece of candy

67

Phonics

long a Words

- Circle the **long a** words in each sentence.

Dog (gave) Cat
8 pieces of (cake).

Dog (made)
a pizza. He
(gave) two
pieces to Cat.

Yes!
Two pieces!

Hooray!

"Hooray!" said Cat.
"Dog (came) here and
(baked) a big cookie."

68

Vocabulary

How Did Cat Say It?

- Write a word from the Word Box to complete each sentence.

Word Box

| yelled | said | begged |

"I like pizza,"
<u>said</u> Cat.

"I want watermelon!"
<u>yelled</u> Cat.

"Please give me
some chocolate milk,"
<u>begged</u> Cat.

69

Skill

Words That Sound the Same

- Some words sound the same, but they are spelled differently, and mean different things.

see 👁 👁   sea 〰

- Write the correct word in each sentence.

| meet | meat |

I will <u>meet</u> you at school.

I had <u>meat</u> for dinner.

| be | bee |

A <u>bee</u> is on the flower.

Will you <u>be</u> home at six?

| here | hear |

<u>Here</u> is a cat.

Please come <u>hear</u> me sing.

70

Answer Key READ Companion Activities

What Word Is Missing?

Write a word from the Word Box to finish the sentences.

Word Box

| called | one | from | little |

Four __little__ monsters swinging from the tree,

__one__ fell off and bumped his knee.

Mommy __called__ the doctor and the doctor agreed,

"No more monsters swinging __from__ the tree!"

89

---

kn Words

Write **kn** on the lines to make words that begin with the /n/ sound.

Then write a **kn** word to finish each sentence.

 k_n_ ee	k_n_ ot
k_n_ ob	k_n_ ife

He bumped his __knee__.

I can make a __knot__.

Mom cut an apple with a __knife__.

Turn the __knob__ to open the door.

90

All in the Family

Label the members of the monster family with the words from the Word Box.

Write a sentence about a family member on the lines below.

Word Box

| Grandfather | Mother | Father | Grandmother |

__Father__

Daddy

__Grandfather__

Grandpa

__Grandmother__

Grandma

__Mother__

Mommy

Sentences will vary.

91

Boy and Girl Monsters

Write **he**, **she**, **his**, or **her** in each box.

This is a little girl monster.

__She__ is purple.

__She__ fell and bumped __her__ knee.

This is a little boy monster.

__He__ is blue.

But __his__ nose is green and __his__ hair is black.

__He__ is swinging from the tree.

92

125

Answer Key
Sentence Skills
Words Every Reader Must Know

PAGE 99:

1. I **think** that is good.
2. Tom and I **went** for a walk.
3. What is that **thing**?
4. Please **come** over here.
5. Cat wants the **most** food.

PAGE 100:

1. **Where** is he?
2. Two boys live over **there**.
3. Which book is **that**?
4. Her dog is bigger **than** my dog.
5. She has a **pretty** name.

PAGE 101:

1. We want **another** dog.
2. There are **five** cats.
3. This is **too** hot to eat.
4. Pat came **to** my house.
5. Did you **find** the toy?

PAGE 102:

2. Here is my school.
3. Do you like dogs?
4. She can leave soon.

PAGE 103:

1. I know about it.
2. How old are you?
3. Please take this box.
4. It goes right here.

PAGE 104:

1. My mother took me home.
2. Did you put that away?
3. Please close the door.
4. Should we go home now?

PAGE 105:

1. We will leave at night.
2. He likes to run fast.
3. Can she buy a book?
4. Come with me to school.

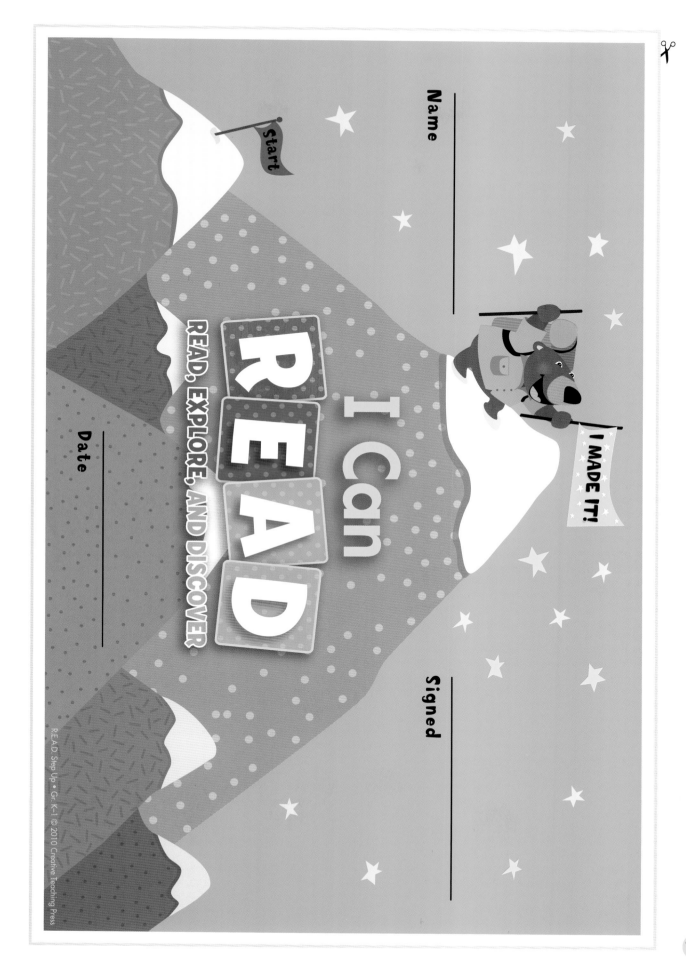

I Can
READ
READ, EXPLORE, AND DISCOVER

Start

I MADE IT!

Name

Date

Signed

READ Step Up • Gr. K-1 © 2010 Creative Teaching Press